CW00925206

Welcome
to the
Museum

ENTER HERE

Fungarium

Illustrated by KATIE SCOTT

Written by DAVID L. HAWKSWORTH, LAURA M. SUZ,
PEPIJN W. KOOIJ, KARE LIIMATAINEN, TOM PRESCOTT,
LEE DAVIES and ESTER GAYA

B P P

Preface

Fungi are probably the least known and most misunderstood organisms on Earth. More closely related to animals than plants, they impinge on almost all aspects of our lives. They are also amazingly varied, from the microscopic to the bizarre.

Fungi are all around us; even as you read this you will be breathing in some microscopic fungal spores from the air. Life would not be the same without them, yet we know barely 5 per cent of the 2.2–3.8 million fungal species on Earth. Species new to science are continually being found, not just in remote tropical forests but even in the UK. Their vast extent has only come to light in the last few years from molecular studies. These have revealed that there are staggeringly huge numbers of species that have never been seen – and are known only from their DNA.

Professor David L. Hawksworth CBE
Royal Botanic Gardens, Kew

Entrance

Have you heard about the 'zombie fungi' that can take control of insect bodies? How about the poisonous mushroom that has the potential to kill cancer cells? Welcome to *Fungarium* – a museum dedicated to the mysterious kingdom of fungi.

Tour the galleries and learn why fungi are more related to humans than plants. Discover how they evolved. Find out about their amazing variety of shapes and colours, some of them alien-like and disgustingly smelly, others incredibly beautiful. The illustrations in this book are not to scale because fungi vary so much in size. Some are microscopic while others are surprisingly large – the giant elm bracket at Royal Botanic Gardens, Kew (page 28) had a bracket with a circumference of around 5m!

Discover which fungi have provided life-saving drugs, which are safe to eat and which are poisonous. Let *Fungarium* reveal all about fungi, their exquisite forms, fascinating lifestyles, and importance to the world we live in.

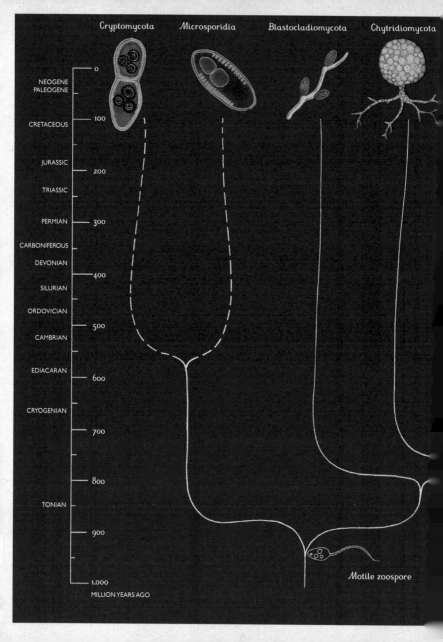

Cryptomycota   Microsporidia   Blastocladiomycota   Chytridiomycota

NEOGENE
PALEOGENE

0

CRETACEOUS

100

JURASSIC

200

TRIASSIC

PERMIAN

300

CARBONIFEROUS

DEVONIAN

400

SILURIAN

ORDOVICIAN

500

CAMBRIAN

EDIACARAN

600

CRYOGENIAN

700

TONIAN

800

900

1,000

MILLION YEARS AGO

Motile zoospore

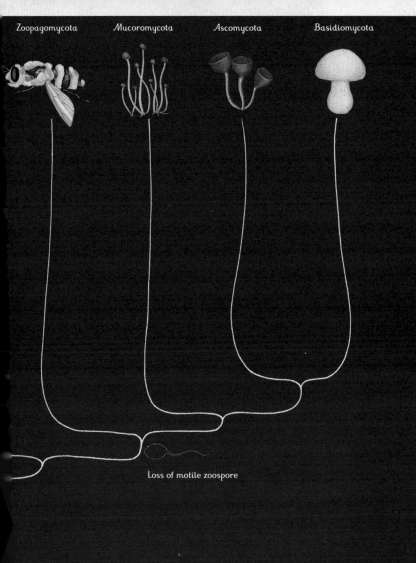

Zoopagomycota Mucoromycota Ascomycota Basidiomycota

Loss of motile zoospore

The Tree of Life

All species on Earth are related and connect together in a 'tree of life', but what does the fungal tree of life look like?

This is a difficult question to answer. Sometimes similar-looking fungi are not at all closely related. Also, because a large proportion of species are still awaiting discovery, it is difficult to build an understanding of historical relationships of the kingdom Fungi.

DNA is helping us to understand how the branches of the fungal tree fit together, including the discovery of new branches such as the Cryptomycota and Microsporidia. These two early groups were originally thought not to contain chitin, a key feature of fungi (see page 10), but DNA later proved this wrong. Other groups, including downy mildews (Oomycota) and slime moulds (Myxomycota) have been proved to not belong to fungi.

The earliest fungi are thought to have evolved around one billion years ago and to have been simple, single-celled organisms that lived in water. Around 700 million years ago the evolutionary transition from aquatic to land-dwelling fungi is estimated to have taken place. Ascomycota and Basidiomycota are the two fungal groups able to form highly complex spore-bearing structures. These groups formed around 600–700 million years ago and together contain the vast majority of known fungal species – around 140,000.

Research on the fungal tree continues and a whole new 'invisible dimension of fungal diversity' in our soils, bodies and waterways is being explored – the so-called dark taxa.

What is a Fungus?

Historically, fungi were treated as plants and studied by botanists. They were included in *Species Plantarium* by the famous naturalist Linnaeus in 1753. But fungi aren't plants: they don't make food by photosynthesis, they don't have roots and they reproduce with spores. Lichens are not plants either; they are a collaboration between a fungal element and a photosynthesising algae (known as a photobiont).

Fungi are in fact more closely related to animals than plants. Just like the outer skeletons of insects and crustaceans, fungal cell walls are made largely of chitin. However, while animals ingest their food by engulfing or swallowing, fungi secrete enzymes that dissolve food outside their bodies and absorb the nutrients through their cell walls. Another difference is that animals move around to search for food, while fungi grow towards it.

Key to plate

1: **Bird's nest fungus**
Cyathus striatus

2: **Red marasmius**
Marasmius haematocephalus

3: **Pixie-cup lichen**
Cladonia chlorophaea

4: **Leathery goblet**
Cymatoderma elegans

5: **Veiled lady**
Phallus indusiatus

6: **Enokitake mushroom**
Flammulina velutipes (cultivated form)

7: **Turkeytail fungus**
Trametes versicolor

8: **Golden shield lichen**
Xanthoria parietina

9: **Fly agaric**
Amanita muscaria

10: **Lane Cove waxcap**
Hygrocybe lanecovensis

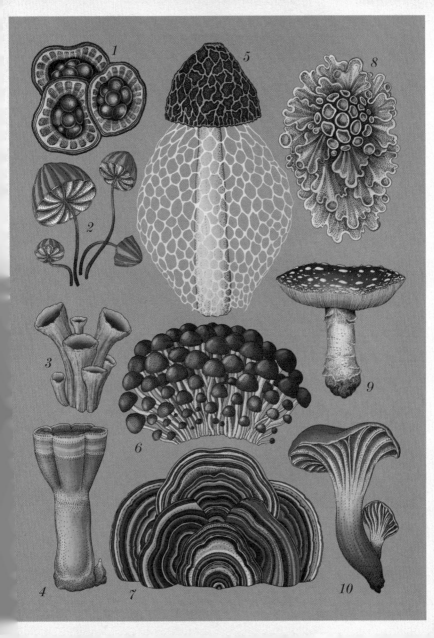

Types of Fungi

Just like animals and plants, fungi have their own kingdom, but it's not as well known. New species are constantly being discovered and scientists think of the estimated 2.2 to 3.8 million species on Earth, fewer than 5 per cent have been identified.

There are at least eight phyla (major groups) of true Fungi: Cryptomycota, Microsporidia, Blastocladiomycota, Chytridiomycota, Zoopagomycota, Mucoromycota, Ascomycota and Basidiomycota. Some of the most ancient are single-celled and don't look at all like typical fungi. Most familiar fungi belong to Ascomycota and Basidiomycota, which produce septate hyphae (typical fungal filaments) and can include mushrooms, yeasts and those fungi that associate with algae to form lichens.

─────────────── *Key to plate* ───────────────

1: **Rozella sp.**
(Cryptomycota)
Motile zoospore

2: **Rhizophydium planktonicum**
(Chytridiomycota)

3: **Piromyces communis**
(Chytridiomycota)

4: **Berwaldia schaefernai**
(Microsporidia)
Spore (sporoblast)

5: **Black bread mould**
(Mucoromycota)
Rhizopus stolonifer

6: **Darwin's fungus**
(Ascomycota)
Cyttaria darwinii

7: **Caesar's mushroom**
(Basidiomycota)
Amanita caesarea

8: **Upright coral**
(Basidiomycota)
Ramaria stricta

9: **Cladia aggregata lichen**
(Ascomycota)

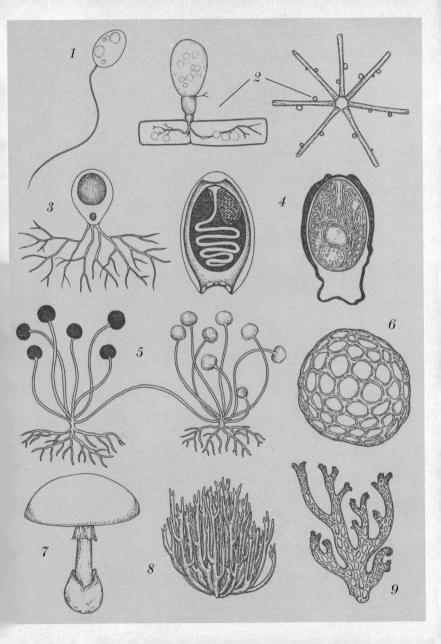

Sexual Reproduction

Fungi can reproduce both sexually and asexually. This is rare and caused great confusion in the past because each reproductive form would often be named as a distinct species. Even today, scientists sometimes use DNA to identify reproductive 'pairs' of the same fungus.

Sexual reproduction in fungi can only be seen with a microscope. Two nuclei, each with a single set of chromosomes, must fuse together. It is a complex process that involves cell division and the exchange and rearrangement of genes. Living organisms including fungi do this because it ensures genetic diversity, fundamental to evolution and ultimately survival. The fusing nuclei can be from the same individual, or different ones of the same species. Once nuclei are fused, they remain in special cells from which new spore-producing structures arise. The new spores will form new fungal colonies.

--------------------------- *Key to plate* ---------------------------

1: **Common field mushroom**
Agaricus campestris
a) Development of a mushroom
b) Part of a gill showing basidia and basidiospores.

2: **Common jellyspot fungus**
Dacrymyces stillatus
Fork-shaped, branched basidia.

3: **Common rust fungus**
Phragmidium violaceum
The stalked spore includes a row of four cells with two nuclei each.

4: **Zygorhynchus sp.**
a) The process of hyphae forming a zygosporangium
b) Zygosporangium and zygospore formed

5: **Candlestick or candle snuff fungus**
Xylaria hypoxylon
As in most ascomycetes, the asci (sacs) contains eight spores.

6: **Dog lichen**
Peltigera canina
Produces asci with a special form of spore discharge.

14

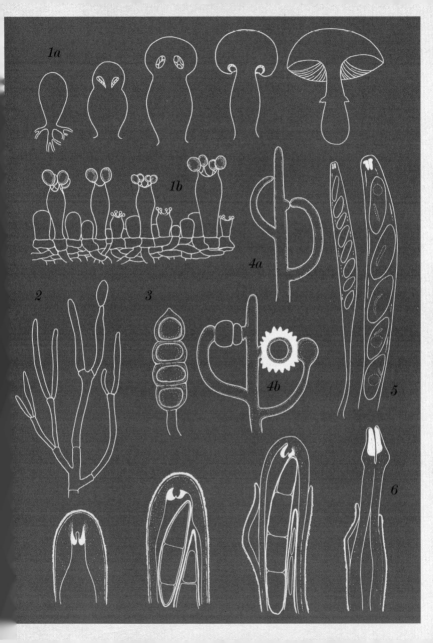

Asexual Reproduction

Many fungi can establish new colonies without sex. This is called asexual reproduction. Some fungi produce both asexual reproductive structures as well as sexual ones, while others have no sexual structures at all. The advantage of an asexual strategy is that it can produce massive numbers of genetically identical spores, which can rapidly grow on new sites.

Asexual spores are produced by simple cell division and their nuclei have just one set of chromosomes. The most common type of asexual spores are conidia, which form from specialised cells in a mind-blowing number of ways. Conidia can form individually, in chains or ball-like clumps and can either be dry or produced in slimy droplets, depending on how they disperse (see page 18). In most cases asexual spores do not travel as far as sexual spores, and only a small proportion end up being widely disseminated by air currents or wind. These are mainly species producing large numbers of small dry spores that often cause allergies.

──────────── *Key to plate* ────────────

1: Alternaria alternata
A plant pathogen that
causes leaf spot.

2: Coemansia erecta
Microscopic saprobes that can
be found in dung and soil.
a) asexual structures
b) spore-bearing structures

3: Thielaviopsis basicola
This plant pathogen can cause
devastating crop diseases.
a) simple tube-shaped condiophores
b) septate brown spores

4: Periconia byssoides
This species can be found on
dead plants.
a) general view of conidiophore
b) magnified view of conidiophore

5: Lasiodiplodia theobromae
This plant pathogen causes rotting in
many tropical crops after harvest.

6: Tetracladium sp.
An aquatic fungi.

7: Parmelina pastillifera
Soralia and isidia are the most
common asexual structures in lichen.

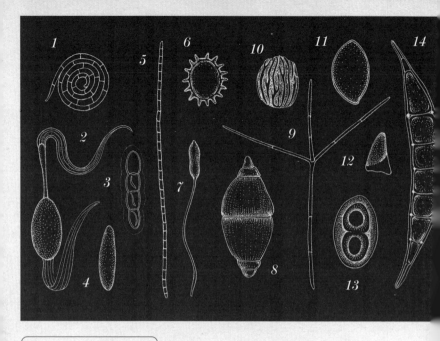

Spores

Spores are reproductive cells produced by fungi. The diversity of fungal spores, both sexual and asexual, is truly amazing, from single cells of just a couple of micrometres (a unit of measurement 0.001 millimetres long, shown as µm) to huge ones visible to the naked eye.

Spore shapes are extremely varied in size and shape. Colours vary from transparent to white, pink or various shades of brown to black.

The form of the spores, and whether they are dry or slimy, depends on their method of dispersal. Some stick together to form massive projectiles, which, when ejected, can travel half a metre or more, while others split into part-spores and establish new colonies. Some are specially adapted to dispersal by insects, birds or mammals. For example, truffles produce their

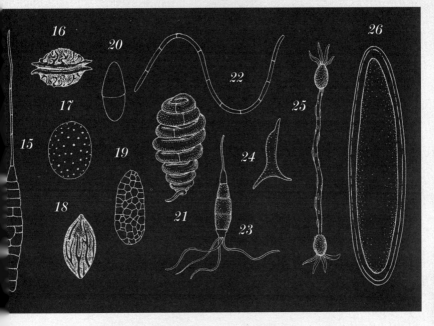

spores in sporing bodies below ground that release a special aroma to attract mammals and help dispersal. Some elaborate spores with long arms are adapted to disperse in water.

--- *Key to plate* ---

1: **Helicomyces scandens** (20µm)
2: **Podospora fimiseda** (360µm)
3: **Sporormiella leporina** (35µm)
4: **Xerocomus badius** (12µm)
5: **Schizoxylon ligustri** (125µm)
6: **Russula viridofusca** (12µm)
7: **Harknessia spermatoidea** (120µm)
8: **Caryospora callicarpa** (75µm)
9: **Tetrachaetum elegans** (250µm)
10: **Ustilago koenigiae** (12µm)
11: **Lophotrichus ampullus** (10µm)
12: **Triangularia bambusae** (25µm)
13: **Rinodina confragosula** (28µm)
14: **Corollospora lacera** (65µm)

15: **Alternaria sesami** (400µm)
16: **Penicillium baarnense** (6µm)
17: **Gelasinospora micropertusa** (40µm)
18: **Neurospora lineolata** (20µm)
19: **Calenia monospora** (65µm)
20: **Neonectria ditissima** (12µm)
21: **Helicoon ellipticum** (40µm)
22: **Anguillospora longissima** (240µm)
23: **Pestalotiopsis guepinii** (45µm)
24: **Cornutispora lichenicola** (15µm)
25: **Zygopleurage zygospora** (285µm)
26: **Pertusaria pertusa** (220µm)

Note: measurements shown are length or longest axis

Growth

All filamentous fungi are made from narrow, cylindrical tubes called hyphae. Filled with liquid that is kept under high pressure by taking in water through their walls, they can act as hydraulic rams, puncturing the surfaces of leaves and forcing themselves through soils, woods and even rock surfaces! Their branching patterns vary according to the availability of food. Not all fungi form hyphae all of the time, or even at all — yeasts are single-celled and divide by 'budding' while some fungi can produce hyphae when invading tissue.

Fungal growth rates vary enormously with humidity and temperature being the key. Pin moulds such as *Mucor* species can cover a slice of damp bread in a few days, while a lichen fungus on a rock may only increase a few millimetres a year. Human pathogens will grow best at body temperature, while fungi of hot deserts favour mid-40s Celsius. Growth rates are of practical importance too. They can help date how long an object (even a corpse) has been in a place, or in the case of lichens, when a roof was built.

--- *Key to plate* ---

1: **Blue mould rot fungus on apple**
Penicillium expansum
When growing on a nutrient-rich surface like an apple, the hyphae of this fungi branch repeatedly in a radial manner, forming circular patches.

2: **Toxic black mould, seen growing on cellulosic material**
Stachybotrys chartarum
This species occurs in warm, damp conditions and has been linked to health issues in humans and animals.

3: Trichoderma viride **seen on a culture plate displaying typical radial growth**
Some fast-growing species of this genus can be cultivated to combat the spread of fungal pathogens in plants including cotton and sugar cane.

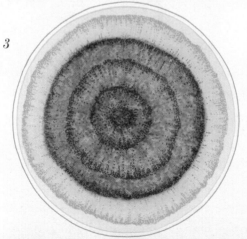

Ecosystem: Mountains

From peak to base, and across snow-covered landscapes, bare stone and luscious forests, mountains provide a diverse range of environments for fungi; some of which cannot be found anywhere else in the world. Harsh conditions caused by the altitude mean the fungi that live here must adapt.

Above the treeline, the alpine zone is characterised by short, open vegetation (mostly grasses and small woody plants), low temperatures and high exposure to sun and wind. Here, the ground is covered by snow most of the year. Fungi here can only fruit during the short period of time after the snow melts. The most abundant ectomycorrhizal fungi here include webcaps, fibrecaps, milkcaps and brittlegills. Equally abundant are crust-like fungi including *Tomentella,* found under rocks, on soil or decaying wood.

At lower elevations, conditions are less harsh, and trees can grow in deeper and richer soils. In the litter layer in the forest, other mycorrhizal fungi such as boletes can be seen. The stinking parachute, a tiny fungus, can also be found in forests. Despite its small size, it smells strongly of rotten cabbage.

———————————————— *Key to plate* ————————————————

1: **Alpine webcap**
Cortinarius alpinus

2: **Alpine brittlegill**
Russula nana

3: **Favre's fibrecap**
Inocybe favrei

4: **Gassy webcap**
Cortinarius traganus

5: **Yellow stagshorn**
Calocera viscosa

6: **Weeping bolete**
Suillus granulatus

7: **Orange birch bolete**
Leccinum versipelle

8: **Stinking parachute**
Gymnopus perforans

Cup Fungi

Cup-shaped spore-bearing fruit bodies, often known as 'apothecia', mostly belong to the ascomycetes group of fungi. Despite their relatively simple structure, they have an enormous variety of forms, many of which are eye-catching and beautiful. Some are extremely tiny (less than a millimetre in diameter), while others can reach 10cm or more. They are often brightly coloured, and some have short or long stalks, while others have eyelash-like hairs. Many lichens (see page 40) also produce tiny cups to spread their spores.

Most cup fungi are spore shooters. The inside of the cup is lined with spore-bearing tissue and when the cup is mature and the weather conditions are just right, spores are shot out at high speed in a synchronised 'puff'.

This diverse group is found in a wide range of habitats from beaches to scorched earth, from animal dung to dead plant matter, and even appears on carpets and the walls of houses. Most live and feed on dead plant material or soil, and in turn become food for other organisms such as insects. Some even form mutually beneficial relationships with tree roots, or with plants such as mosses (see pages 36-39).

--------------------------------- *Key to plate* ---------------------------------

1: **Spring orange peel fungus**
Caloscypha fulgens

2: **Plectania chilensis**

3: **Eyelash fungus**
Scutellinia scutellata

4: **Cookeina speciosa**

5: **Scarlet elf cap**
Sarcoscypha austriaca

6: **Hare's ear**
Otidea onotica

7: **Black earth tongue**
Trichoglossum hirsutum

8: **Orange peel fungus**
Aleuria aurantia

9: **Green elf cup**
Chlorociboria aeruginosa

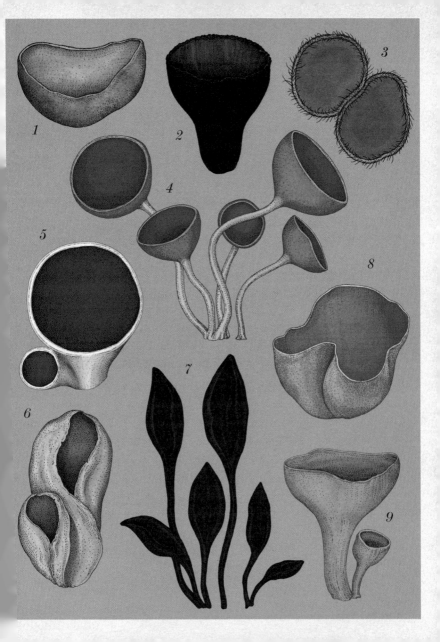

Mushrooms and Toadstools

'Mushroom' and 'toadstool' are not scientific terms but are used to describe spore-boring fruit bodies with a similar appearance, those we often see growing in soil or on wood. Mushrooms are fleshy and have a cap, gills and a stipe (stem). Sometimes the word 'mushroom' is only used for edible fungi, though it can apply to toadstools as well. The word 'toadstool' is usually applied to fungi that are inedible or poisonous and comes from the medieval idea that toads, considered carriers of poison, liked to sit on them.

An interesting phenomenon which occurs only in mushrooms is fairy rings. These appear when mushrooms or toadstools grow in an arc or ring. They can be found in woodlands and grasslands and are produced by over 50 different species including the edible fairy ring fungus (*Marasmius oreades*).

One of the most colourful mushroom groups is the waxcaps (*Hygrocybe* spp.). Their sporing bodies can be wonderful shades of red, orange, yellow, green or pinkish purple.

━━━━━━━━━━ *Key to plate* ━━━━━━━━━━

1: **Shaggy ink cap**
Coprinus comatus

2: **Fly agaric**
Amanita muscaria

3: **Shaggy scalycap**
Pholiota squarrosa

4: **Violet webcap**
Cortinarius violaceus

5: **Waxcaps**
Hygrocybe spp.
a, b, c, d) As shown here, waxcaps are bright spots of colour, often seen on long-established grasslands and lawns. Some grassland waxcaps are especially rare.

6: **Blue roundhead**
Stropharia caerulea

Bracket Fungi

While most mushrooms produce their spores inside gills, bracket fungi (or polypores) form sporing bodies with pores or tubes on their underside. In most cases, they are as hard as the wood of the trees they grow on. They make shelf- or bracket-shaped, or – more rarely – circular bodies that are often called 'conks'. Like most mushrooms they belong to the Basidiomycota.

Bracket fungi are wood decayers, growing mainly on tree trunks and branches, but a few exceptions can form mycorrhizas (see pages 36–39) with trees. They are the only organisms able to break down the tough compounds that make up lignin found in wood. This means that without bracket fungi (and their relatives, corticioid fungi, or 'crust fungi' which can be found on the undersides of dead tree trunks or branches), forests would be covered in wood and leaf litter. That is why they are vital for nutrient cycling and carbon dioxide release in forest ecosystems. On the other hand, some of them are severe pathogens of trees, and are major causes of damage to timber.

Bracket fungi have been used by humans since ancient times. The tinder fungus (*Fomes fomentarius*) has been used to make clothing such as caps as well as tinder, while chaga (*Inonotus obliquus*) is believed to suppress cancer progression and enhance the immune system. This species looks like burnt coal and can be found on the trunks of mature birch trees.

--- *Key to plate* ---

1: **Giant elm bracket**
Rigidoporus ulmarius

2: **Beefsteak fungus**
Fistulina hepatica

3: **Oak polypore**
Buglossoporus quercinus
Underside of bracket
This rare species is found on
ancient oaks and is under threat.

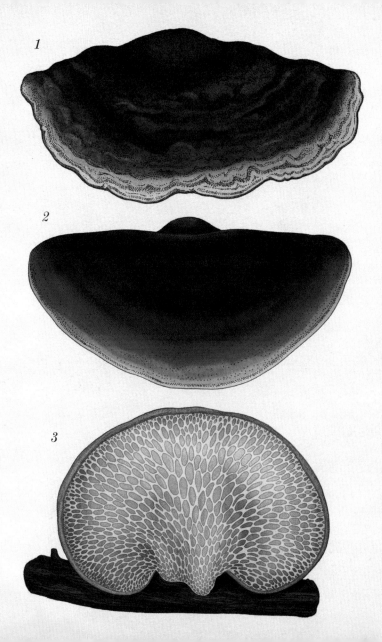

Gasteromycetes

Gasteromycetes share similar reproductive strategies, even though they are not closely related. They usually obtain their food by breaking down organic material in the soil and therefore play an important role in the ecosystem by recycling nutrients. They are not able to forcibly disperse their spores from gills or pores, instead they produce spores on the inside of their fruiting bodies and use different methods to disperse them, resulting in unusual and striking forms.

Puffballs use the simplest form of dispersal. They all have round sporing bodies and for some, the spore-rich mass on their inside needs physical help to be pushed out, being knocked by an animal for example. Other puffballs have small holes out of which spore masses can be puffed out, while others simply split open. Bird's nest fungi use raindrops to disperse their spores while the weird and wonderful stinkhorn family all produce a brownish, spore-rich liquid called gleba. Gleba is foul-smelling and attracts certain insects who then fly away with the gleba stuck to them.

--- *Key to plate* ---

1: **Common puffball**
Lycoperdon perlatum

2: **Sculpted puffball**
Calvatia sculpta

3: **Bird's nest fungus**
Cyathus striatus

4: **Stinkhorn fungus**
Colus hirudinosus

5: **Earthstar fungus**
Geastrum quadrifidum

6: **Veiled lady**
Phallus indusiatus
A member of the stinkhorn family.

7: **Common earthball**
Scleroderma citrinum
a) the spore-bearing interior, or gleba
b) exterior

8: **Rounded earthstar**
Geastrum saccatum

Foliicolous Fungi

In tropical forests, many leaves look like they have beautiful mosaics on their surfaces; these are mostly fungi. The trees are evergreen and their leaves can be very large and live for many years so benign fungi, known as 'foliicolous', use them as places to live.

Unlike plant pathogenic fungi, foliicolous fungi don't invade or kill the leaves, though they can have special bodies that attach to the surface. They gain nutrients from the water dripping from the forest canopy, not from the leaves they grow on. A number are lichen-forming and capture leaf-dwelling green algae to secure a supply of sugars. As non-lichen fungi do not need light to photosynthesise, some groups only grow on the underside of leaves.

While mainly a feature of the humid tropics, there are a few foliicolous species able to grow on evergreen leaves in temperate regions, including box, holly, juniper and laurel.

--- *Key to plate* ---

1: Meliola urariae
Typical branching of hypha which attach the fungus to the leaf.

2: **Leaf**
Seen with a mixture of fungal colonies on its surface, including lichens.

3: Strigula orbicularis
a) Sporing bodies and thallus
b) Section of a sporing body with plant cuticle layer on top and epidermal cells in a layer below

4: Tricharia urceolata
Species of *Tricharia* lichen produce hair-like structures named 'hyphophores'.

5: Parenglerula macowaniana
a) Example of mycelium growth on a leaf
b) Section of a sporing body on a leaf

6: **Shield fungus**
Lichenopeltella palustris
A specialised flattened sporing body.

7: Peltistroma juruanum
Colonies of fungus growing on a leaf.

Ecosystem: Temperate Forests

With fertile soils, plenty of rain and seasonal weather, temperate forests are ideal homes for fungi.

Oak and beech are common deciduous trees found in these forests and fungi play an important role by decaying organic matter (saprotrophs), enhancing tree growth by forming symbiotic relationships with their roots (see pages 36–39) or associating with algae and cyanobacteria to form lichens. Some saprotrophs are root-inhabitants of these trees, such as the zoned rosette. Others can be found on trunk heartwood, on lower branches of living trees and on fallen wood including chicken of the woods and beefsteak fungus.

Fungi can also signal environmental conditions. The oak milkcap is an indicator of high nitrogen pollution and soil acidification while the lichen tree lungwort thrives in ancient woodlands with low pollution levels.

───────────────────── *Key to plate* ─────────────────────

1: **Oakmoss lichen**
Evernia prunastri

2: **Chicken of the woods**
Laetiporus sulphureus

3: **Beefsteak fungus**
Fistulina hepatica

4: **Zoned rosette**
Podoscypha multizonata

5: **Spindle toughshank**
Gymnopus fusipes

6: **Oak milkcap**
Lactarius quietus

7: **Clustered bonnet**
Mycena inclinata

8: **Yellowfoot or trumpet chanterelle**
Craterellus tubaeformis

9: **Coral fungi**
Ramaria sp.

10: **Beech or slimy milkcap**
Lactarius blennius

11: **Common earthball**
Scleroderma citrinum

12: **Matt bolete**
Xerocomellus pruinatus

13: **Tree lungwort**
Lobaria pulmonaria

Mycorrhizas

Hidden to our eyes most of the time and living in the soil under our feet, there are fungi that make associations with plant roots, forming mycorrhizas. These are ancient, symbiotic relationships between certain fungi and most plants on Earth. These relationships evolved millions of years ago to help the first plants establish and successfully grow in nutrient-poor environments. Even now, 90 per cent of the plants on Earth still cannot live without these fungi in their roots.

Mycorrhizal fungi colonise the roots of plants and provide them with water and nutrients from the soil that they can't access themselves. In return, the fungi obtain plant carbohydrates which they need to grow. Different fungi associate with different plants forming four main types of mycorrhizas: arbuscular, ectomycorrhizas, ericoid and orchid.

--- *Key to plate* ---

1: **Cross section of a root showing the four main types of mycorrhizas**
a) **Orchid mycorrhizas:** the seeds of orchids do not have nutrients so orchids rely on fungi to germinate.
b) **Arbuscular mycorrhizas:** formed by 80 per cent of plants by fungi specialising in the uptake of phosphorus.
c) **Non-mycorrhizal**
Root with no fungal tissue present
d) **Ectomycorrhizas:** formed by woody plants such as oaks and pines, ectomycorrhizal fungi specialise in the uptake of nitrogen.
e) **Ericoid mycorrhizas:** this type of fungi colonise the roots of plants of the Ericaceae family (including

heathers and blueberries), unlocking nutrients for their host plants.

2: Cenococcum geophilum
a) This ascomycete colonises the roots of over 200 different plant hosts.
b) Instead of sporing bodies, dormant structures called sclerotia remain in the soil for hundreds of years.

3: **Saffron milkcap**
Lactarius deliciosus
a) The orange mushroom is the edible sporing body, and is only seen in autumn.
b) How fungus looks in the roots of pine, forming ectomycorrhizas.

Mychorrhizal Networks

Mycorrhizal fungi are connected to the roots of their host plants forming mycorrhizas. These extend into the soil through their fungal filaments. One fungus can be attached to the roots of many plants (of the same or different species) and one plant can be attached to many different fungi. In this way, plants can be connected to each other through their roots by these fungi, forming the 'wood wide web'.

The interconnected filaments that the fungi form can be vast. Sometimes we see evidence of them above ground in the form of sporing bodies such as mushrooms or crusts, and below ground in the form of truffles but these are just the tip of the iceberg. Below ground are very complex communication networks. A gram of soil can contain hundreds and hundreds of fungal filaments, and they all help gather nutrients and water from the soil that plants would otherwise be unable to reach.

─────────────────────── *Key to plate* ───────────────────────

1: **Mature English oak and young seedlings**
Quercus robur

2: **Sporing bodies**

3: **Ectomycorrhizas and fungal filaments**

Lichens

Lichens are the result of highly successful relationships between fungi (mycobionts) and at least one other photosynthesising organism (photobiont) so an alga, a cyanobacterium or both. The fungus benefits from the sugars produced by the photobiont, and the photobiont gets a place to live, physical protection and better access to mineral nutrients. Lichens are so well integrated that they were historically studied as one single species. Today, we know that nearly one fifth of all known fungal species form lichens. More than 98 per cent belong to the largest fungal phylum, Ascomycota, with a few species classified within Basidiomycota.

Lichens come in a wide range of shapes and colours and grow on almost any surface they can find: rocks, bark, soil and even cars! Compared to other groups, they grow extremely slowly (from less than a millimetre to a few centimetres a year), but research shows they can survive for centuries. Lichens thrive in extreme conditions. This means they are sensitive to pollution and are therefore excellent indicators of air quality.

--- *Key to plate* ---

1: Cora pavonia

2: **Brown-eyed wolf lichen**
Letharia columbiana

3: **Map lichen**
Rhizocarpon geographicum

4: **British soldiers' lichen**
Cladonia cristatella

5: **Bullseye lichen**
Placopsis gelida

6: **Beard lichen**
Usnea florida

7: **Umbrella basidiolichen**
Lichenomphalia umbellifera

8: **Shield lichen**
Parmelia sulcata

9: **Golden-eye lichen**
Teloschistes chrysophthalmus

10: Tephromela atra

11: **Pin lichen**
Calicium viride

Entomogenous Fungi

Entomogenous fungi harm, infect and may kill insects. Because they occur naturally, some are used as safe pest control. For example, *Beauvaria bassiana* grows naturally in the soil and causes white muscardine disease which gives insects a white fluffy look. It is used as an insecticide to control insects such as termites, white flies, aphids and many other species that damage plants. The spores are mixed in a solution and then sprayed on the affected plants.

A particular group of entomogenous fungi, most belonging to the genus *Ophiocordyceps*, has become known as 'zombie fungi'. They can be found worldwide and while it's not known how many species there are, many infect just one type of insect. These fungi release chemicals into the insects' brains forcing them to climb higher up in trees and plants. The fungus then grows rapidly in the insect's body, creating sporing bodies. Being higher up means the spores can be spread more widely.

--- *Key to plate* ---

1: **Dong Chong Xia Cao**
Ophiocordyceps sinensis

2: **Weevil fungus**
Ophiocordyceps curculionum

3: **Wasp fungus**
Ophiocordyceps humbertii

4: **Ant fungus**
Pandora formicae

5: **Zombie ant fungus**
Ophiocordyceps unilateralis

6: **Caterpillar fungus**
Cordyceps militaris

7: **White muscardine disease**
Beauveria bassiana

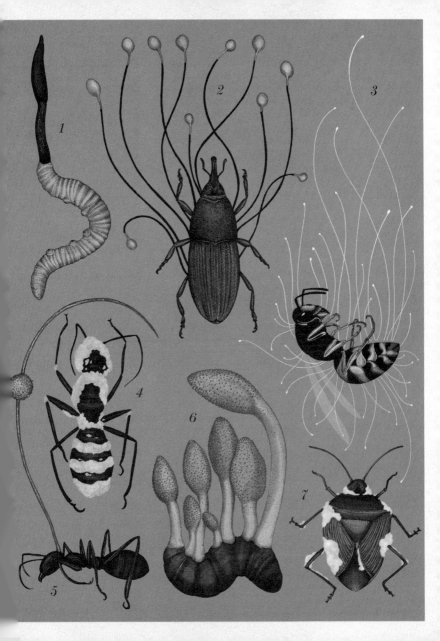

Ants and Termites

Ants and termites have been farming fungi for millions of years but because these insects evolved separately, they grow their food in different ways.

Every year when termites build new nests, the *Termitomyces* fungus produces mushrooms on the termites' old nests. The termites collect spores released by the mushrooms when they crawl out of their new nests, and use them to regrow their fungus gardens. Scientists call this 'horizontal transfer'. To grow their fungus, the termites dig long underground tunnels through which they carry dead plant material. They eat the material and then grow the fungus on their own faeces.

In contrast, when new ant queens leave their old nest, they take a little bit of fungus with them. The queens store the fungus in a pouch inside their mouth (called the infrabuccal pocket) until their next nest is completed. Scientists call this 'vertical transfer'. Thousands of leaf-cutting ants walk in long lines through the rainforest each carrying pieces of leaves. When they get back to their nest, they chew the leaves into little balls and give this to the fungus to grow on.

------------------------------ *Key to plate* ------------------------------

1: **Termite mushroom**
Termitomyces striatus

2: **Ant mushroom**
Leucoagaricus gongylophorus
Mushrooms from the ant fungus are a rare sight and the ants try to remove them when they grow.

3: **Fungus-growing termite**
Macrotermes natalensis

4: **Termite mound**
Macrotermes natalensis

5: **Leaf-cutting ant**
Atta cephalotes

6: **Ant food**
Leucoagaricus gongylophorus
The fungus the ants cultivate grows nutritious structures called gongylidia. They are packed with sugars and fats to feed the ants.

Early Mycologists

In classical times it was believed that lightning strikes produced mushrooms, and even during the mid-eighteenth century, naturalists didn't understand fungi very well. The first person to make real progress was the Italian Pier Antonio Micheli (1679–1737), who proved that spores could produce new fungi. However, Carl Linnaeus (1707–1778), the 'father of modern taxonomy', inadvertently hindered the study when he included fungi within the plant kingdom.

Early mycologists also investigated organisms such as downy mildews and slime moulds, both of which we now know are not true fungi. Reverend Miles Joseph Berkeley (1803–1889), the founder of British mycology, shot to fame for his investigations into the cause of the potato blight – which led to the Great Famine in Ireland (1845–1849). Berkeley confirmed the cause was the organism we now know as *Phytophthora infestans*, a downy mildew.

Arthur Lister (1830–1908) and his daughter Gulielma (1860–1949) meanwhile spent some 50 years carefully observing and illustrating slime moulds, producing the exquisitely and lavishly illustrated book, *Monograph of the Mycetozoa*. Since these early observations our understanding of the fungal kingdom has continued to evolve and now we have a better idea of what a fungus is (see page 10).

───────────── *Key to plate* ─────────────

1: **Potato blight**
Phytophthora infestans
a) Leaves and b) potato affected by symptoms c) Sporangia with sporangiophores

2: **Slime moulds**
Slime moulds belong mostly to a group called 'Amoebozoa.'

a) *Physarum polycephalum* in plasmodium stage
b) *Physarum* sporing structures
c) *Comatricha typhoides*
d) *Comatricha nigra*
e) *Leocarpus fragilis*
f) *Dictyostelium discoideum*
g) *Hemitrichia calyculata* in three stages of development

Plant Pathogens

Although most fungi perform helpful roles in recycling nutrients in ecosystems, some are harmful to the plants they interact with. Fungi that attack plants (fungal plant pathogens), are a major cause of crop damage. This means the price we pay for food is dependent on our success in the ongoing struggle to control these fungi.

While new plant pathogens are always emerging, our knowledge of them dates back to antiquity and continues to guide us today. Fungal rust diseases were first described by a student of Aristotle, Theophrastus, but seventeenth century farmers in Europe observed a connection between barbary plants and the damage to wheat caused by stem rust. Once it was known that barberry is a host for the wheat stem rust, simply digging up and destroying the barbary plants controlled the disease. A similar fungal disease, rice blast disease, is one of the most destructive in the world. It destroys enough rice a year to feed 60 million people.

Fungi adopt three broad strategies when infecting plants. They can infect plants and live off their nutrients while keeping the plants alive (biotrophs), they can kill plants outright and digest the dead plant matter (necrotrophs) or they can start out as biotrophs but then switch to a necrotrophic lifestyle later. Once they have infected plants, fungal pathogens interfere with the plant's ability to defend itself.

─────────────── *Key to plate* ───────────────

1: **Basal stem rot**
Ganoderma orbiforme

2: **Rice blast disease**
Pyricularia oryzae

3: **Dutch elm disease**
Ophiostoma novo-ulmi

4: **Witches' broom disease**
Moniliophthora perniciosa

5: **Dark honey fungus**
Armillaria ostoyae

Poisonous Fungi

Despite their reputation, only about 120 species out of 22,000 mushroom producing species are poisonous and of real concern; a mere 0.5 per cent. Another 90 species can cause stomach upsets in some people, and some 150 have hallucinogenic properties.

Most instances of poisoning occur when a toxic mushroom is mistaken for its edible cousin, for example the toxic false morel closely resembles the edible true morel (see page 52). Mistaking the two can cause nausea, vomiting and even death. In the case of the death cap, the toxins attack the liver and symptoms may not appear for a day or so after it is eaten. Great care must therefore always be taken when collecting mushrooms to eat.

Particularly interesting is the effect of the substance ergotamine produced by *Claviceps* species, especially *Claviceps purpurea*, which sprouts from the ears of cereals and other grasses. Ergot poisoning is one of the oldest known examples of fungal poisonings and in Europe in the thirteenth to fourteenth centuries, when rye grass was a staple crop used in bread, whole communities were poisoned. Ergotamine interferes with the nervous system, causing hallucinations, itching and burning sensations. It also constricts blood vessels and can cause gangrene.

Key to plate

1: **Satan's bolete**
Rubroboletus satanas
a) Exterior view b) Interior view

2: **Kaentake**
Trichoderma cornu-damae

3: **Ergot fungus**
Claviceps purpurea
a) Magnified view of sporing body

b) Ergots seen on rye

4: **Destroying angel**
Amanita virosa

5: **Death cap**
Amanita phalloides

6: **False morel**
Gyromitra esculenta

Edible Fungi

Humans have a long history of eating fungi. We know that mushrooms have been a food source since at least the Stone Age, but they were likely eaten earlier.

Globally at least 350 species of fungi are collected for food (the most common being boletes, milkcaps, brittlegaps and chanterelles) but wild mushroom gatherers must be careful since some edible mushrooms can cause allergic reactions and some closely resemble poisonous species. Over the centuries we have learned by trial and error which fungi are edible, and scientific study can help. The ugly milkcap (*Lactarius turpis*), for example, was once considered to be edible, but is now known to contain a compound that causes genetic mutations.

The global market for edible mushrooms is worth about 43 billion pounds sterling a year and includes both wild and cultivated mushrooms. Almost all cultivated species are decomposers, and grow easily in dead organic matter, for example button mushrooms. However, many of the flavoursome gourmet species, like porcini, are mycorrhizal which means they live in relationships with plants and are therefore very hard to cultivate.

─────────────── *Key to plate* ───────────────

1: **Matsutake**
Tricholoma matsutake

2: **Button mushroom**
Agaricus bisporus

3: **Chanterelle**
Cantharellus cibarius

4: **Black truffle**
Tuber melanosporum

5: **Caesar's mushroom**
Amanita caesarea

6: **True morel**
Morchella esculenta

7: **Baker's yeast**
Saccharomyces cerevisiae

8: Penicillium roqueforti

9: **Zeller's bolete**
Xerocomellus zelleri

10: **Cabbage lungwort**
Lobaria linita

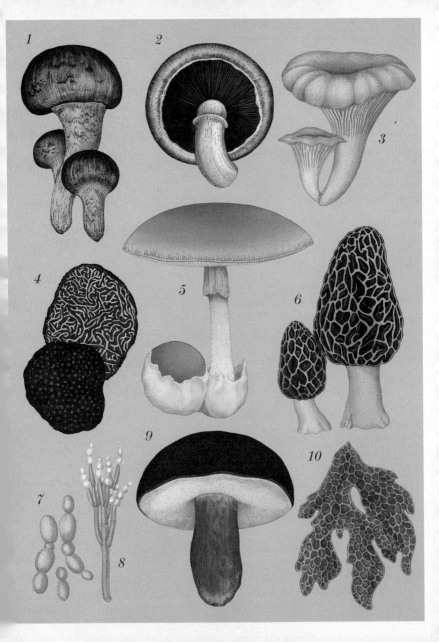

Wonder Drugs

Fungi are the source of some of the most important drugs ever discovered, most famously, penicillin. Around the world, scientists conduct fungi research in the hope of finding the next life-saving drug.

The story of penicillin starts in the London laboratory of the microbiologist Alexander Fleming (1881–1955) in the 1920s. Fleming's Petri dish contained a culture of *Staphylococcus* bacteria but was also accidentally contaminated with the mould *Penicillium rubens*. Fleming noticed that the *Staphylococcus* could not grow near the mould and wondered if it was producing some kind of inhibitory chemical. Follow-up work by Howard Florey (1898–1968) and his team at Oxford identified the inhibitory substance as penicillin and demonstrated its incredible powers for treating bacterial infections.

Fungi have also proved to be a fantastic source of immunosuppressants. The important compound, cyclosporine, for example, made organ transplantation possible by preventing the body from rejecting the transplanted organ. There are also the statin drugs, used to lower cholesterol, whose founding member lovastatin was isolated from the mould *Aspergillus terreus*.

So, where will the next fungal wonder drug be found? Perhaps it could come from the unlikely source of the death cap (see page 50)? The toxin which makes the mushroom so dangerous – a-Amanitin – is being researched because of its potential to attack cancer cells.

───────────────── *Key to plate* ─────────────────

1: Glarea lozoyensis
Colony seen growing on culture plate

2: Penicillium rubens
a) Colonies growing on a culture plate
b) Appearance under light microscope

3: Tolypocladium inflatum

4: Aspergil erreus
a) Colony seen growing on culture plate
b) Appearance under light microscope

5: Isaria sinclairii
Infected cicada nymph

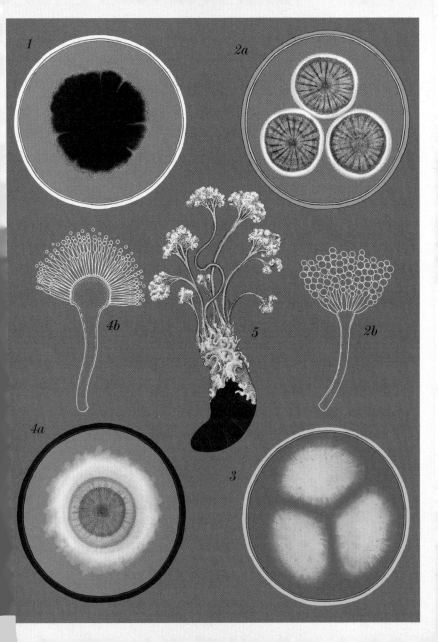

Ecosystem: Tropical Forests

Step into a tropical rainforest and the first thing you notice is its lush and diverse vegetation, with many different leaf shapes and tree heights. The trees grow extremely densely, and, green all year round, there is no autumnal flush of mushrooms. Instead, fungi are seen sporadically throughout the year.

While boreal and temperate forests (see pages 22 and 34), mainly feature ectomycorrhizal trees (see pages 36–39), those in tropical forests have fewer links with endomycorrhizal fungi. This does not affect the amount of fungi present however. The tropics contain many more plants than temperate regions and are therefore an amazing source of unexplored fungal diversity.

Leaves of many tropical trees live for several years, and develop a patchwork of specialised microscopic fungi, including lichen-forming species (see page 32). Huge tree trunks can be covered by mosaics of shade-loving crustose lichens and the vast quantities of wood and leaf litter on the forest floor are broken down by fungi, for example, the *Cookeina* species.

―――――――――――― *Key to plate* ――――――――――――

1: **Pleurotus djamor**

2: **Letrouitia domingensis**

3: **Deflexula subsimplex**

4: **Christmas wreath lichen**
Herpothallon rubrocinctum

5: **Spotted cort**
Cortinarius iodes

6: **Amethyst deceiver**
Laccaria amethystina

7: **Indigo milkcap**
Lactarius indigo

8: **Golden-scruffy collybia**
Cyptotrama asprata

9: **Cobalt crust**
Terana coerulea

10: **Pycnoporus sanguineus**

11: **Pod parachute**
Gymnopus montagnei

12: **Cookeina speciosa**

13: **Lactocollybia aurantiaca**

14: **Red marasmius**
Marasmius haematocephalus

15: **Parrot waxcap**
Gliophorus psittacinus

Glossary

Algae An informal term referring to a group of unrelated eukaryotic organisms that lack typical land plant tissues (stems, leaves, stomata). They live in water or in humid habitats.

Asci A sac-like structure in which spores develop. Only ascomycete fungi produce asci.

Basidia A microscopic club-shaped spore-bearing structure produced by basidiomycete fungi.

Bracket A spore-bearing structure that is fan- or shelf-shaped. It is of tough consistency and can be found growing on tree trunks.

Cap The top part of the mushroom that sits on the stalk.

Chitin The structural material that forms the exoskeletons of insects and also the main component of fungal cell walls.

Chromosome Thread-like structures in which the DNA is packaged in the nucleus.

Crustose Forming or resembling a crust.

Filament A very fine, threadlike structure.

Gills The part of the mushroom where spores are made. Gills are usually found under the cap.

Hypha Each of the fine, branching threads, or filaments, that make up the mycelium of a fungus.

Lichen Lichens form symbiotic relationships between fungi and at least one photobiont (an alga, a cyanobacterium or both). They can grow almost everywhere.

Micrometer A unit of measurement, 0.001 millimetres long, written as μm.

Mould A type of fungus that thrives in moist or humid environments. It can sporulate without producing mushrooms or any special spore-bearing structures.

Mushroom The reproductive part of some fungi, the mushroom is a spore-bearing structure with a cap, gills and stipe.

Mycelium The main body of most fungi, made up of a network of hyphae.

Mycorrhiza Fungi that grow in close interaction with plant roots, establishing a mutually beneficial partnership.

Nuclei The membrane-bound structures that contain the cell's genetic material.

Pathogen An organism that causes disease, and can kill its host.

Saprotroph Any organism that lives and feeds on dead organic matter.

Spore A small cell produced by some fungi, plants (moss and ferns), algae and bacteria. Spores are involved in both sexual and asexual reproduction. They can disperse by wind, water droplets or animals.

Stipe The upright stalk, or stem-like part of a mushroom, which raises the cap above the ground and connects it to the mycelium.

Truffle An underground, closed, rounded spore-bearing structure.

Yeast A microscopic single-celled fungus that lives in colonies.

Zoospore A small cell involved in asexual reproduction that is able to move independently because of an appendage called a flagellum.

Zygosporangium
A specific type of sporangium, or structure, which produces zygospores.

Zygospore
A thick-walled spore that is formed through sexual reproduction in certain types of fungi, and can remain dormant for long periods of time until the environmental conditions are suitable.

Index

To Learn More

Mycological Societies
British Lichen Society http://www.britishlichensociety.org.uk/
British Mycological Society https://www.britmycolsoc.org.uk
Fungus Conservation Trust http://www.abfg.org/
International Association for Lichenology http://www.lichenology.org
International Mycological Association http://www.ima-mycology.org/

The Fifth Kingdom
An online version of Bryce Kendrick's popular textbook.
http://mycolog.com/fifthtoc.html

Species Fungorum
This initiative gives current names for fungal species. For unfamiliar names, this is the must-go-to site.
http://www.speciesfungorum.org/

Royal Botanic Gardens, Kew
Learn about Kew's global and collaborative scientific work. Kew houses the world's largest fungarium with over 1.25 million dried specimens from all over the world.
www.kew.org/science-conservation
https://www.kew.org/science/collections-and-resources/collections/fungarium

State of the World's Plants and Fungi (2020)
Prepared by international scientists, published by Kew.
https://stateoftheworldsfungi.org/

US National Fungus Collections
Held by the US Department of Agriculture including collections previously held by the Smithsonian Institution.
https://data.nal.usda.gov/dataset/us-national-fungus-collections

Westerdijk Fungal Biodiversity Institute Utrecht, The Netherlands
This institute maintains around 100,000 cultures of fungi and hosts the MycoBank database owned by the International Mycological Association.
http://www.wi.knaw.nl
http://www.mycobank.org

Curators

Katie Scott is illustrator of the bestselling *Animalium* and *Botanicum*, which was also produced in collaboration with the Royal Botanic Gardens, Kew. *Animalium* was chosen as the *Sunday Times* Children's Book of the Year, 2014. Katie studied illustration at the University of Brighton and is inspired by the elaborate paintings of Ernst Haeckel.

Ester Gaya is a senior research leader at Kew. She began her career in mycology in Spain and after some time in the USA decided to settle in the UK. She has spent the past 20 years researching fungi. She is especially fascinated by lichens and tries to understand their evolution.

David L. Hawksworth CBE has wide pure and applied mycological interests. He was the last Director of the International Mycological Institute, is an Honorary President of the International Mycological Association and an Honorary Research Associate of the Royal Botanic Gardens Kew.

Laura M. Suz is a research leader in mycology at Kew. She has spent almost 20 years digging up tree roots and looking at their ectomycorrhizas. Laura did her PhD in Spain on edible truffles. She moved to London in 2010 to investigate the fungi that associate with oak and the threats to their diversity.

Pepijn W. Kooij has studied fungus-farming ants for almost 10 years in the hot tropics of Panama. Born in the Netherlands, he spent his visits to the zoo looking at leaf-cutting ants. He did his PhD in Denmark. In 2015, he moved to London to prove that it is not fungus-farming ants, but rather ants-farming fungi.

Kare Liimatainen is a Finnish mycologist with a PhD from the University of Helsinki who has also worked in Sweden and the United States. Working with colleagues he has found dozens of new fungal species in the UK over the last four years. His happiest memories are of trips to North America where he was surrounded by masses of beautiful fungi.

Tom Prescott is a research leader at Kew. His work focuses on investigating the natural chemicals found in plants and fungi, with a special focus on their effects on human cells and the model fungal organism *Saccharomyces cerevisiae*. He also travels to Papua New Guinea to research medicinal plants.

Lee Davies comes from a palaeontology and invertebrate fossil background. After a stopover working on tropical African plants, he has become Kew's mycology curator.

BIG PICTURE PRESS

First published in the UK in 2023 by Big Picture Press,
an imprint of Bonnier Books UK
4th Floor, Victoria House, Bloomsbury Square, London WC1B 4DA
Owned by Bonnier Books
Sveavägen 56, Stockholm, Sweden
www.bonnierbooks.co.uk

1 3 5 7 9 10 8 6 4 2

ISBN 978–1–80078–423–9

This book was typeset in Gill Sans and Mrs Green.
The illustrations were created with pen
and ink and coloured digitally.

Designed by Winsome d'Abreu and Lee-May Lim
Edited by Victoria Garrard and Joanna McInerney
Production by Neil Randles

Printed in China

This book was produced in consultation with plant and fungal experts at the
Royal Botanic Gardens, Kew. With thanks to: Bill Baker, Paul Cannon, Mark Chase,
Martin Cheek, Colin Clubbe, Phil Cribb, Aljos Farjon, Lauren Gardiner, Olwen Grace,
Aurélie Grall, Tony Kirkham, Bente Klitgaard, Carlos Magdalena, Mark Nesbitt,
Rosemary Newton, Lisa Porkny, Martyn Rix, Paula Rudall, Dave Simpson, Rhian Smith,
Wolfgang Stuppy, Anna Trias-Blasi, Jonathan Timberlake, Tim Utteridge,
Maria Vorontsova, Jurriaan de Vos, James Wearn, Paul Wilkin.

With special thanks to Gina Fullerlove and Lydia White, Kew Publishing.

MIX
Paper from
responsible sources
FSC® C178225